M E
LOC

Writte

R. BARNARD WAY

Ian Allan Ltd

INSIDE THE CAB
OF A LOCOMOTIVE

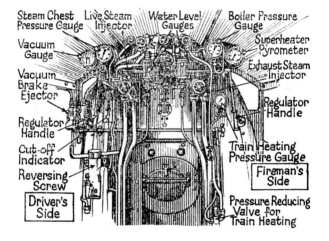

This drawing illustrates the interior of one type of locomotive cab. The arrangement of the controls and the positions of the crew vary according to the designs of the different Railway Regions.

MEET THE LOCOMOTIVE

Something like six thousand years ago the Wheel first came into use to help men to move their heavy loads more easily. Nobody knows quite how it came about. Certainly rollers were used by the ancient Assyrians. Just as certainly rollers were developed into wheels by the same people. Ever since those days the Wheel has gone on turning to make travel and transport swifter and pleasanter. When the hard road was laid down to bear the wheeled chariot, improvement came quickly, but still the wheel bore only *the load*. This was because those early mechanics had no engine to apply to their wheels. They could think only in terms of animal power to draw the chariots along. For speed they had to limit themselves to that of the swiftest horses; and so it remained for thousands of years.

With the coming of engines in the 18th century, it was not long before their inventors turned their thoughts to the possibility of applying the new-found power of steam to locomotion. They had already discovered that the iron wheel on the iron rail made for easy movement of heavy loads of coal and stone, though horses still trudged along hauling the clumsy wagons. So, the steam locomotive was born.

Leading	Driving	Trailing	TENDER		TANK
4 —	6 —	2	*not counted*	2 — 6 — 4	/ T_

Whyte		2-6-0 + 0-6-2 Garratt	Continental System
0-4-0			
2-4-0			
2-4-2			
4-4-0		Continental System	
4-4-2		"Atlantic"	2.B.1
4-4-4		$\frac{4\text{-}4\text{-}4}{T}$ method of indicating Tank Locos	2.B.2
0-6-0		$\frac{0\text{-}6\text{-}0}{T}$	C.
0-6-2			C.1
2-6-0		"Mogul"	1.C.
2-6-2		"Prairie"	1.C.1
2-6-4			I. C.2
4-6-0			2.C.
4-6-2		"Pacific"	2.C.1
4-6-4		"Baltic"	2.C.2
0-8-0			D.
2-8-0		"Consolidation"	1.D.
2-8-2		"Mikado"	1.D.1
4-8-2		"Mountain"	2.D.1
2-8-4			1.D.2
0-10-0			E.
2-10-0		"Decapod"	1.E.

THE 'WHYTE' WHEEL CLASSIFICATION

WHO INVENTED
THE LOCOMOTIVE?

Many people, when asked who invented the steam locomotive, would answer " George Stephenson." They would give the name of the first locomotive as the worthily famous *Rocket*. Both answers would be wrong. Trevithick, the Cornishman, built three locomotives, the first in 1804, and there were actually 44 various engines built before the *Rocket* appeared in 1829, though it is only fair to add that several of those 44 were Stephenson's.

However, we are concerned with the modern locomotive. Although it is a very far cry from those early machines, it is important to remember that it works in exactly the same way. But now we make them bigger, swifter, more powerful, and we get about ten times more work out of our coal than did the pioneers.

The business of the locomotive is to turn fuel into a form of power that will move wheels on a steel road. This it does with the aid of water. The fuel is burned in a firebox and the heat boils the water into steam. This steam is confined in the boiler until it has attained a good deal of pressure and is then allowed to pass out and escape—but not until it has done some of the work we want. Even with our very best engines we cannot get more than one-tenth part of the power we know to be locked up in the fuel. It is sad to have to admit that there is very little prospect of our ever getting much more than that. Presently we shall see why this is so.

THERE ARE 'TENDERS'
AND 'TANKS' AND
VARIOUS TYPES

First of all we will look at a few locomotives and make sure we know what the outside parts are all about and their proper names. We may divide them first into two classes: those that draw a tender carrying water and fuel and those that carry water and coal supplies on their own wheels. The first we call Tender Engines; the second, Tank Engines.

Now, you don't have to be very observant to see that there is a good deal of difference between one locomotive and another, even after they have been sorted out into the two classes already made. It is not only in the matter of size: some have more wheels; some have a lot more working parts outside; others have a very clean, slick appearance with very little in the way of exposed machinery.

Look first at the drawings on page 7 of some typical British locomotives. One is an express giant with very clean lines and the minimum of external machinery; another, a heavy, slow-moving engine for hauling long trains of coal. Quite clearly they have a lot in common, but, if you bear in mind that the pictures are drawn to the same scale, one distinction must be plain to you immediately—the difference in wheel sizes. This brings us to the next sort of classification.

4 — 6 — 2   Coal   Water
Driving Wheels, 6ft.8ins.   9 tons   5000 galls.

3 cylinders

Express Passenger—pulls 500-ton trains at 70 m.p.h.

2 — 8 — 0   Coal 9 tons: Water
Driving Wheels, 4ft. 8½ ins.   4000 galls.

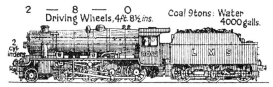

2 cylinders

Heavy Goods—hauls trains of 1,000 tons at 25 m.p.h.

2 — 6 — 0   Coal,   Water
Driving Wheels, 5ft. 0ins.   4 tons   3000 galls.

2 cylinders

This Mixed Traffic Locomotive works Branch
Line trains

0 — 6 — 0
Driving Wheels, 4ft. 7½ ins.

Saddle Tanks hold 1200 galls.

This locomotive does station
shunting duty

**TYPICAL
BRITISH
LOCOMOTIVES**

All four are
drawn to the
same scale

THE WHEEL
CLASSIFICATION

Locomotive wheels are of two sorts: those that do the driving and those that only carry the load, though, of course, the driving wheels carry the load as well. With no load to keep their tyres down on the rails they could not drive. Of the so-called " idle " wheels there are two sorts: leading and trailing. Note that it is not necessary for a locomotive to have any idle wheels at all, or it may have some of one sort and not of the other, but it *must* have driving wheels. Looking at an engine from one side you see, at each axle, one wheel only. But, as you know there is another wheel at the other side on the same axle, the one wheel you see must be reckoned as two, or a group of two reckoned as four, and so on.

Look at the diagram on page 4. It shows the standard classification (known as the Whyte classification after the engineer who devised it) used on most railways in this country. At the top (left) is an engine with two pairs of small wheels in front, three pairs of large driving wheels, followed by a single pair of small wheels. (The tender has three pairs but they are not included for classification purposes.) We call the first group 4, the second 6, and the third 2, so the classification is 4-6-2. If there were no trailing wheels we should put 0 instead of 2 and then would have 4-6-0, the classification of the express engine on page 19. If there were no leading wheels, only the six " drivers," the classification would be 0-6-0. There are thousands of engines of this type hauling freight trains in this country.

THE CONTINENTAL
CLASSIFICATION—AND
THE SOUTHERN'S

Continental engineers, dealing with large electric locomotives—often having many driving wheels, which might be coupled together or not—thought of a different scheme. They reckon axles only or, as you see the engine from one side, the visible wheels. They use figures for idle axles and letters of the alphabet, in consecutive order from A, for driving axles. Wheels coupled together indicate one big motor driving the

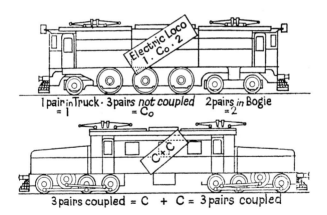

1 pair in Truck · 3 pairs *not coupled*   2 pairs *in* Bogie
= 1   = C$_0$ = 2

3 pairs coupled = C + C = 3 pairs coupled

These diagrams of **electric** locomotives are brought into this book on the **steam** locomotive for a purpose ; to illustrate the Continental classification by axles.

group, but wheels not coupled mean a separate motor
for each axle.   To mark the difference the letter **C**
(*third* in the alphabet) is used for *three* axles coupled,
but, if the axles are not coupled a little o is added,
thus: C_o.   So, on the Continent, a locomotive we show
as 4-6-2 is 2-C-1 with coupled wheels, or $2\text{-}C_o\text{-}1$ with
separate motors.   The diagram on page 9 shows one
or two variations.   Where a *plus* sign is put in it means
that the driving groups are separate and probably in
the form of a bogie.   You may care to figure out
what a $1\text{-}A+B_o\text{-}2$, or a $2\text{-}B_o+B_o+B_o\text{-}2$, look like.

The former Southern Railway introduced a system
based on this, though it indicates first the idle wheels
and then the drivers.   The indication is noted on the
number plates of the engines.   A 4-6-2 engine on the
Southern becomes a 2-1-C.   The 2 gives the leading
axles, 1 gives the trailing axle, and C (being the third
letter of the alphabet) shows three driving axles.   The
number that follows the letter—as in the example
2-1-C-45—is that of the engine itself.   If there are
no idle wheels nothing is denoted for them, so 2-C
means 4-6-0, and C just means 0-6-0.

TYPE NAMES

Type names have been given to some of the engines.
Everyone knows an *Atlantic* or a *Pacific*.   In addition
there are the *Mogul, Prairie, Consolidation, Mountain,
Decapod*.   The American suggestion in most of these
names gives an indication of their origin but they are

freely used in Great Britain. It is more technical to refer to a 4-4-2, a 4-6-2, a 2-10-0, or whatever it may be. In our diagram (page 4) we have some wheel arrangements that have passed out of use now and would only be met by those readers who like to study the old-timers.

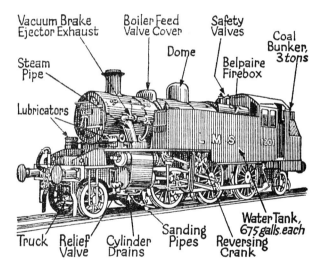

In this picture of a typical modern tank locomotive the various parts seen on the outside of it are labelled. This sort of engine is mostly used on branch line services. Its wheel classification is $\frac{2-6-2}{T}$

HELPING THE LOCOMOTIVE
AROUND CURVES

Before we leave this subject there is another point
to bear in mind.   Every engine has to go round curved
stretches of track at times and it can be imagined that
a long one with many wheels would offer a great resis-
tance to any such movement away from the straight.
To get over this, the idle wheels are often mounted
on a frame pivoted in some way to the main frame
so they swing slightly to make the engine wheelbase
(that is, the distance between the centres of the axles
of the first and last wheels) more flexible on a curve.
Sometimes when there are a good many driving wheels,
flexibility is further improved by having some of the
" drivers " without flanges.   This does not affect the
driving effort of the wheels.

GIVING THE LOCOMOTIVE
THE "WORKS"

We must now consider some other details.   Why do
some engines have a lot of " works " outside and others
not?   They all have much the same machinery, you
may argue, so if it is not outside, then it must be
inside, where it is more difficult to get at for cleaning
and oiling.   Very true.   Engineers nowadays prefer
to put much of it outside in order to help matters.
There was a time when a slick appearance counted
more than ease in maintenance.   Even so, with many

engines, there is just as much unseen as there is outside. A few years ago we saw streamline engines,
with much of the gear enclosed, but one railway group
has given it up and on another some of the enclosing
plating has been removed.

THE FIREBOX

It is time now to take a look at the inside arrangements. These are divided into two parts: one to
generate the power, the other to convert it into motion
at the wheels. We will assume that our engine burns
coal, as most of them do. The firebox is usually made
of thick copper plate and at the bottom is a grid of
iron bars on which the fire is made. Below this is a
box of sheet iron to form an ash-pan and opening
into it are hinged flaps letting in air to the grate. These
flaps, or dampers, can be opened and closed, by levers
in the cab, to control the amount of air admitted.

At its front the firebox, towards the top, opens out
towards the boiler, but the flames have to escape by
way of about 200 steel tubes passing through the boiler
barrel. The water surrounds these tubes and, within
the boiler, flows over the top of the firebox. Here
there must always be a good depth of water. The fireman watches a glass tube in the cab and, so long as he
can see a clear depth in this water-gauge, he knows
all is well.

Two sorts of fireboxes are used on British locomotives: one has a round top so you cannot see at once
where firebox and boiler meet; the other has a square,

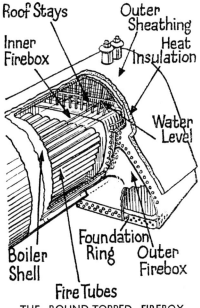

Roof Stays
Outer Sheathing
Inner Firebox
Heat Insulation
Water Level
Boiler Shell
Foundation Ring
Outer Firebox
Fire Tubes

THE ROUND-TOPPED FIREBOX

flat top. This latter is the Belpaire firebox and it has definite advantage in that it does ensure a large quantity of water above the top of the inner box, where heat is most intense.

An arch of firebricks is built over the grate and this deflects the flames, lengthening their path to make sure that burning coal sparks are consumed into hot gas before being pulled through the tubes. The firebox casing you see from the outside is not the same as the inner box in which the fire burns, as the sketch shows.

As the water boils into steam, a great pressure is set up in the boiler. This would squash the firebox flat but for hundreds of copper bolts and stays that hold it strongly to the outer firebox which is made of very strong steel plate. Outside this, the box and boiler are covered with non-conducting material like magnesia, and over this is the sheet steel casing that you can see.

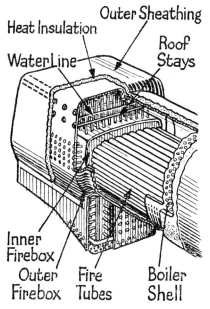

THE BELPAIRE FIREBOX HAS A FLAT TOP

THE SAFETY VALVES

The safety valves are provided to guard against the
pressure rising to danger point.   Powerful springs hold
the valves on to their seatings and these are screwed
down to such a degree that it is only when the steam
pressure gets to the calculated point that they yield.
Once lifted, the valves allow enough steam to escape
to ease the pressure and then snap down again to stop
the outflow.   The pressure must never drop lower than
the working pressure for which the engine is designed.

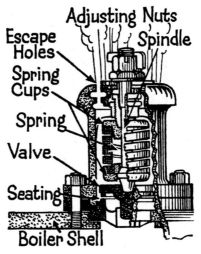

Adjusting Nuts
Spindle
Escape Holes
Spring Cups
Spring
Valve
Seating
Boiler Shell

THE POP SAFETY VALVE IN ACTION

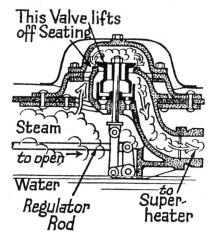

This Valve lifts
off Seating

Steam
to open →

Water

Regulator
Rod

to
Super-
heater

HOW THE STEAM IS PASSED FROM THE
BOILER TO THE SUPERHEATER

THE REGULATOR AND
THE SUPERHEATER

The steam passes out of the boiler barrel on its way
to the engine cylinders through the steam pipe which
begins at the highest part of the boiler, often under
the dome, where the regulator is placed. The reason
for this is to avoid water being carried along with it.
as far as possible. Nowadays all engines have an
arrangement, known as a superheater, which dries this
steam, and, by heating it up to a much greater degree,

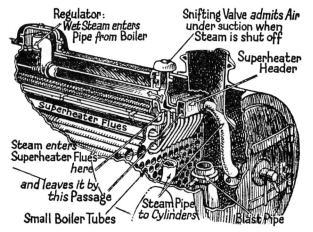

Regulator:
Wet Steam enters
Pipe from Boiler

Snifting Valve admits Air
under suction when
Steam is shut off

Superheater
Header

Superheater Flues

Steam enters
Superheater Flues
here

and leaves it by
this Passage

Small Boiler Tubes

Steam Pipe
to Cylinders

Blast Pipe

THE SUPERHEATER AT WORK

gives it extra working power.   This superheater consists of a number of smaller tubes enclosed in large
flue tubes and the flames pass through them too.   The
superheater header can be seen at the top of the smokebox; from here the steam passes to the cylinders.   Note
that the steam does not go into the superheater until
the driver opens up his regulator.   When steam is shut
off air must be allowed to enter by way of the snifting
valve, usually seen just behind the chimney.

The hot gases from the fire, having passed through
the boiler tubes, can now escape by way of the chimney
—there is no more work for them to do.   This seems
a pity because there is really a vast quantity of heat

remaining. It could be used (and is used sometimes) to heat the cold water passing to the boiler but that is better done in another way by using heat still in the steam after it has done its work in the locomotive, as we shall see.

THE BLAST PIPE
AND BLOWER

To draw up the fire and make it burn fiercely, a draught has to be contrived in the smokebox, otherwise the fire would only burn slowly, without producing the white-hot flame required to generate great volumes of steam quickly. So, when the steam has done its work, it escapes by way of the blast-pipe and sets up a partial vacuum in the smokebox as it goes. This pulls the hot gases out of the firebox and these are replaced by air through the grate so as soon as the engine is going there is a fine, hot fire. When the engine is at a standstill, or steam is shut off for any other reason, the driver uses his blower. This is

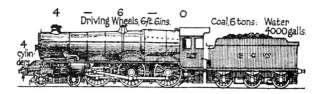

This WR express locomotive has a conical boiler and no dome

simply a jet of steam blown up the chimney from a small pipe fed by the boiler, acting in the same way as the blast pipe. If steam were shut off with the engine travelling fast, the fire might blow back through the firing door with very unpleasant results for the crew but for the blower.

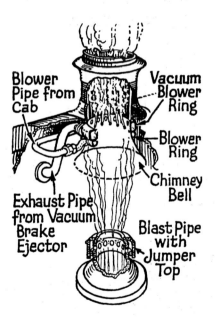

BLAST PIPE, BLOWER AND CHIMNEY

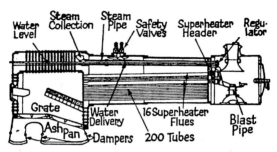

A CONICAL BOILER WITH BELPAIRE FIREBOX

THE TWO
BOILER TYPES

The question is often asked: What is the difference between a straight-topped and a coned boiler?

The pictures help to show this and the sections of boilers illustrate the inside arrangements. The coned boiler allows a large space for the steam to collect in, at the hottest point right over the firebox, making it unnecessary to have a dome—as in the WR loco-motives. With a straight top—seen best in the picture of a superheater on page 18—a dome has to be provided for the collection of the steam. The regulator is put in there as well. With the conical boiler the regulator valve is on the superheater header in the smokebox, as the drawing on page 21 shows. In the days before superheating the collection of steam was important but to-day, when every locomotive has a superheater, it is not quite so critical a matter; it is necessary, however, to make sure that the steam carries with it as little water as possible. This steam is called " saturated " because it is impossible to get it completely clear of water. This was formerly a great nuisance as a lot of water would accumulate in the cylinders and had to be blown out regularly. Now the superheater dries out all the water and actually makes more steam than it receives. Whether a coned boiler or a straight top is better is anyone's guess though the former is certainly the favourite nowadays.

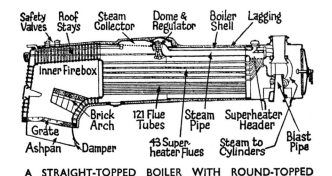

Safety Valves · Roof Stays · Steam Collector · Dome & Regulator · Boiler Shell · Lagging · Inner Firebox · Brick Arch · 121 Flue Tubes · Steam Pipe · Superheater Header · Grate · Ashpan · Damper · 43 Super-heater Flues · Steam to Cylinders · Blast Pipe

A STRAIGHT-TOPPED BOILER WITH ROUND-TOPPED FIREBOX

THE FEED-WATER
INJECTOR

Feeding water into the boiler is done by one of the most ingenious devices ever invented: the injector. There are two kinds: the live steam and the exhaust steam injectors. The principle of both is the same, depending upon jets of steam being chilled to condensation in conical passages. This sets up a vacuum, sucking the water into the passages, imparting to it, owing to the high speed of the jet, a high velocity. So much energy is given to the water that it positively drives its way past a valve into the boiler—even against the full steam pressure in it. This is a remarkable thing, especially when it is done by means of some of the exhaust steam, as is the case when the locomotive is running, for this steam is at a very low pressure indeed.

The live steam injector valve may be in the cab, but both live and exhaust steam injectors are usually below the footplate. They discharge the water into the boiler by separate valves, which may be at the side, as on many SR engines, or on top. The pipes are easily recognised and are marked in certain of our illustrations. On LMR and WR engines the feed is on

(Continued on page 26)

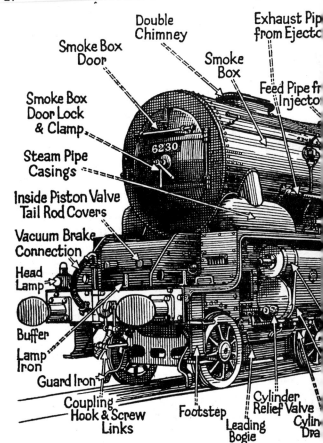

Double Chimney

Smoke Box Door

Smoke Box

Exhaust Pip from Ejecto

Smoke Box Door Lock & Clamp

Feed Pipe fr Injecto

Steam Pipe Casings

6230

Inside Piston Valve Tail Rod Covers

Vacuum Brake Connection

Head Lamp

Buffer

Lamp Iron

Guard Iron

Coupling Hook & Screw Links

Footstep

Leading Bogie

Cylinder Relief Valve

Cylin Dra

THE EXTERNAL, VISIBLE PARTS OF

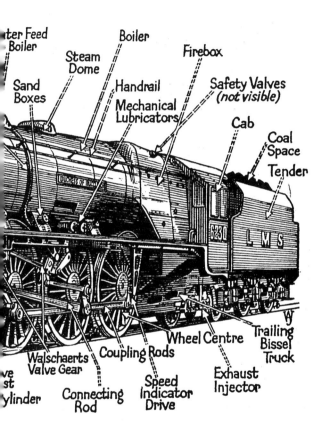

ter Feed
Boiler

Boiler

Firebox

Steam
Dome

Sand
Boxes

Handrail

Safety Valves
(not visible)

Mechanical
Lubricators

Cab

Coal
Space

Tender

Wheel Centre

Trailing
Bissel
Truck

Walschaerts
Valve Gear

Coupling Rods

Exhaust
Injector

Speed
Indicator
Drive

Connecting
Rod

- 6 - 2 **L M R E X P R E S S L O C O M O T I V E**

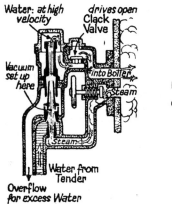

Water: at high velocity — drives open Clack Valve

Vacuum set up here — into Boiler — Steam

Steam

Water from Tender

Overflow for excess Water

THE
ESSENTIALS
OF A LIVE
STEAM
INJECTOR

the top of the boiler, the pipes following the contour up to the dome, where the non-return or clack valve is situated. The safety valves are under the same dome as the clack valve in the case of Western Region locomotives.

Injectors will only work with cold water, as that is needed to condense the steam jet, so we are not able to conserve heat by using a feed-water heater. Those readers who remember their physics know about the latent heat of steam, that great store of heat that steam carries with it. This represents by far the greatest part of the heat put by the fire into the boiler, and is not used by the engine at all, but blown out of the chimney or through the safety valve. Now, with the injector, this latent heat passes into the feed water, making it hot almost to boiling point as it goes past the clack valve into the boiler. So we do save a little after all. This latent heat difficulty is what we were principally thinking of when we mentioned at the beginning the little hope of ever getting more than one-tenth of the power available in our fuel. Even in the best of our electricity generating stations, where everything is done for efficiency in ideal conditions, they do very well to get 25 per cent. But do not run away with the idea that the modern locomotive is a poor affair from the scientific point of view on this account. It is very far from that. It does a large part of the world's work on fuel that once costing very little now costs a lot, causing us to look into the efficiency rates much more quizzically than we used to do.

Some years ago experiments were carried out on British locomotives with feed-water heaters, very much favoured by American and Continental engineers. These fittings use the latent heat of the exhaust to heat up the water, but it has then to be forced into the boiler by a pump as hot water will not work in an injector at all. We do not know whether any of these are still at work, but many of them have been discarded in favour of the well-tried and reliable injectors.

Well now, we have got our steam at the superheater header, at a pressure maybe of 250 lb. to the square inch and a temperature of 615 deg. Fahrenheit. (By the way, lead melts at 621 deg.) We have now to exploit the pent-up energy as well as we possibly can, and as quickly, to save loss. A big boiler will deliver steam like this at the rate of about 15 tons an hour.

Thus we arrive at the second half of the locomotive: the machinery part that everyone can see doing its work.

CYLINDER
AND PISTON

First we take a cylinder, which is just a round box, shaped like a can, and in it slides a piston, which is made to fit very closely, yet to run to and fro easily. A rod fixed to the piston passes out through one end

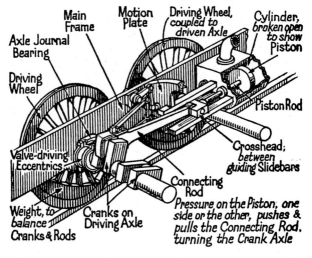

How the mechanical principles of the steam engine are applied to the locomotive

of the cylinder by way of a steam-tight hole—called
a gland. Holes at each end of the cylinder allow the
steam to get in and out. To the end of the piston rod
we hinge a long rod that bears upon the crank that
turns the axle. The diagram on page 30 makes this
plain. In it we have cut open the cylinder to show
the piston too. If the piston is pushed one way the
crank is turned. Then, if the piston is pushed back,
the crank goes on turning. So, to and fro goes the
piston, and round and round goes the axle, and the
driving wheel goes with it.

THE VALVES AND
THE STEAM PORTS

To produce this to and fro—or reciprocating—movement of the piston we have to open and close the steam
holes or ports in the cylinder at the proper times, and
this is the work of the rather elaborate gear of rods
and links seen outside the wheels on many engines.
Think first of one side of the piston only and refer
to the diagram. The steam flows into another cylinder
at the top of the engine cylinder, with the ports cut
right through at each end. There are two pistons on
one rod, so they work together and cover or open the
ports as they move. The outer ends of the top cylinder
—or valve chest—open out to exhaust pipes and so to
the blast pipe.

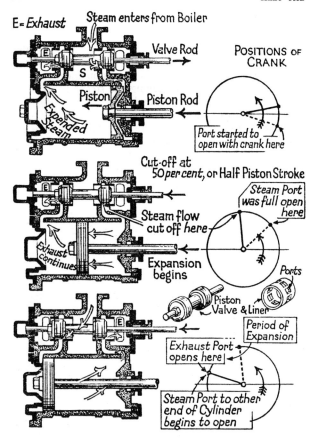

E = *Exhaust*

Steam enters from Boiler

Valve Rod

POSITIONS OF CRANK

S

Piston

Piston Rod

Expended Steam

Port started to open with crank here

Cut-off at 50 per cent, or Half Piston Stroke

Steam Port was full open here

Steam flow cut off *here*

Exhaust continues

Expansion begins

Ports

Piston Valve & Liner

Period of Expansion

Exhaust Port opens here

Steam Port to other end of Cylinder begins to open

WHAT GOES ON IN THE CYLINDER AND VALVE CHEST DURING A PISTON STROKE

In the drawing, when the right-hand *valve* piston moves to the right, it uncovers the steam port and allows steam to pass through to the main cylinder and drive the piston to set the engine in motion. When some steam has entered, the valve piston moves to the left, closing the port and leaving the steam to expand, continuing to drive the main piston. Just before the end of the stroke the valve passes right over the port, opening it up to the exhaust so the steam, finding an easy escape, ceases to press forward.

Now think of the opposite end of the cylinder. The valve at that end uncovers the port to steam at just about the same moment, so the piston is driven back again, clearing all the steam out of the end of the cylinder at which we first looked. Exactly the same order of things continues at each end of the cylinder at exactly timed intervals. The speed depends upon several factors, first of which is the work the engine has to do, but chiefly upon the amount of steam allowed to pass. This depends upon the opening of the regulator valve by the driver.

Modern locomotives are designed to use the expanding power of steam and a good driver will so cut down the amount passing to the cylinders that no more than a twentieth part of the cylinder volume is filled with steam before the valve cuts it off. This " cut-off " is often quoted as a percentage when locomotive runs are being described. The remaining volume is filled by the expansion of the steam which, you must remember, has been squeezed into a very small space and is bursting to get out and push something out of its way.

Think of it in this way: a typical cylinder of a big British locomotive will be about 16 inches in diameter —there will be four of them. A little arithmetic tells us that the area of each piston is a little more than 200 square inches. The entering steam comes in at about 240 lb. pressure and this actually gives a push of 21 tons at the beginning of the stroke, which is kept up for just as long as the port remains full open. As the steam expands, this push falls off, but is still strong enough to do the work, even when well expanded.

Oddly enough, the driver keeps the regulator valve wide open all the time, or nearly so, that the engine is

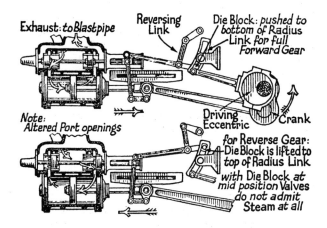

How linking-up and reversing are carried out on the Walschærts Valve Gear

working. The cut-off of steam is varied by the reversing lever which alters the distance travelled by the piston valves, thus limiting the amount of opening of the ports. At hardly any time will the valves be open for more than a quarter of the piston stroke, even with the engine working its hardest, though most engines are so designed that the valves could be kept open for about three-quarters of the stroke.

VALVE GEARS

One of the illustrations (page 34) shows the valve motion, invented by Walschærts, a Belgian engineer, and named after him. It has been adopted in place of the Stephenson gear by most railway engineers, as it is more suitable for use outside the engine, and it gives a slightly improved movement to the valves. The varying cut-off is brought about by sliding the radius rod up or down in the swinging link. *Right down* means full forward gear, *mid-way* no movement of the valves at all, and *upwards*—reverse. Each cylinder usually has its own valve gear, but in some engines one gear serves two cylinders. Some ex-LNER locomotives with three cylinders have what is called a conjugated gear, a very clever device that combines the movements of the outside gears into one suitable for the inside cylinder.

The steam distribution we have described is called " inside admission " because the steam comes in at the middle, between the piston valves. Some engines have the opposite arrangement, the steam entering from the outer ends and exhausting at the middle. This is called "outside admission." Recognising the difference would be a rather technical job for anyone but the expert, and is not really important during the first study of the locomotive.

On inside cylinder engines the Walschærts gear is usually driven by an eccentric, but on outside cylinder

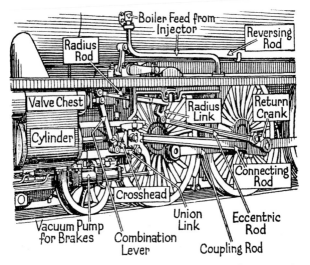

The parts of the Walschærts Valve Motion as fitted to the Southern Region "King Arthur" class locomotives. There are several variations of this motion.

engines it is driven by a crank built outside the crank pin that drives the wheel, which gives the same movement as an eccentric.   An eccentric is a circular block fixed to the axle out of centre.   A ring slides on it freely in a groove, with a rod fixed to it.   When the axle turns, the rod is given a to and fro movement just as a crank would work it.   Stephenson's valve gear has two eccentrics for each cylinder, one for forward and the other for backward driving.   It is still used for many engines with inside cylinders.

" COMPOUNDING "

There is a good system which was much in favour from time to time in this country, and still is elsewhere, by which the exhaust steam from one set of cylinders passed into another set of larger ones to do still further work.   This is called " compounding."   Suppose the steam pressure is 200 lb. per square inch and we expand it in a cylinder 19 inches in diameter until it has dropped to 85 lb.   There is a lot of work it still can do, but to give the same push to a piston as those 200 pounds did we should require a big piston two-and-a-half times the area.   That would make a rather larger cylinder necessary, so the exhaust steam is taken from one high pressure cylinder and turned into two others, each one-and-a-quarter times the area, 21 inches in diameter.   Though these figures are not absolutely exact, they give an idea of one system, as used on the compounds of the LMR (a very good lot of 4-4-0 engines still doing hard work).   Several different arrangements have been tried, but British railway engineers do not employ the principle very much and the only examples we have left are old designs.

We have given a good deal of attention above to valves and valve gears. That is because steam distribution is the one thing that can either make or mar the engine, however good the boiler may be. Great attention is given to setting the valves of the engine when it is being built or repaired, and it is the work of a highly-trained mechanic.

Other kinds of valves are also seen, as well as other forms of valve-driving motions. On some Southern Region engines there is a new gear, based on an old type, driven by chains from the axle. Some LNER-built engines have poppet valves, something like those on motor car engines. These are driven by a turning shaft geared from the driving wheel axle.

COUPLING RODS

Mention of driving wheels brings us to another important feature. One pair of wheels would be quite insufficient to get enough grip upon the rails to move a heavy train, in spite of the 20 tons or more that they may be supporting. So the other driving wheels are coupled up to this pair by coupling rods, one on each side, set at right angles in most cases. When one wheel turns, the others are compelled to turn with it, so we have perhaps six or eight wheels to help with their grip on the rails.

The express engine that has to travel fast has large driving wheels. But on an engine that has only to haul heavy loads at moderate or low speeds, the wheels are smaller. An express engine will have driving wheels of 6ft. 6in. or more in diameter but the freight engine will have them about 5ft. In between these are the mixed traffic engines able to cope with a variety of loads, not quite equal to the highest speeds of the express fellows, but fully up to their loads or more. They have wheels of about 6ft. diameter. Tank engines for fast suburban services have smaller wheels, say about 5ft. 3in. These give them a good chance when frequent stops have to be made, accelerating quickly to get a good speed in between stations.

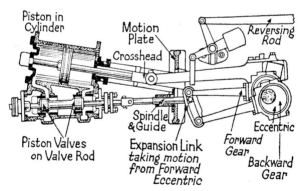

The parts of Stephenson's Valve Motion. Although this motion is not frequently used, it can be found on many engines with inside cylinders.

MORE ABOUT
FIREBOXES

Talking of wheels brings us back to the point where we started. Many will want to know why a pair of small wheels trail behind the driving wheels. If the " drivers " are so important, why not have another pair instead of the small wheels, thus giving the engine extra hauling power? A good question, but one that is easily answered. It is because a good firebox must be deep and, for preference, wide as well. A wide firebox simply will not fit in between the tall driving wheels and a deep one must go down as low as possible. In this way the 4-4-2 and the 4-6-2 locomotives were developed, the low trailing wheels allowing the designer all the space he wanted to put in a full-size firebox unhampered by the wheels. The trailing wheels just carry the extra weight and they are usually arranged to pivot a little to allow for passage around curves.

It is true that many WR engines have fireboxes between their driving wheels. But on the comparatively narrow grates good Welsh coal is burned. How much good coal counts is shown by the fact that

engines of equal power on some other lines—those
having to burn coal of inferior quality to best Welsh
—must have firebox grates at least a quarter larger
in area, about 50 square feet as against 34 square feet
of the Western Region *Kings*.

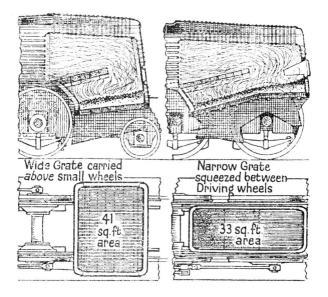

Wide Grate carried
above small wheels

41
sq. ft.
area

Narrow Grate
squeezed between
Driving wheels

33 sq. ft.
area

The two sorts of firebox : (left) wide box supported by a
pair of trailing wheels ; (right) narrow and long box fitted
between 6 ft. 6 in. driving wheels. Both locomotives are
of the same power.

ARTICULATED
LOCOMOTIVES

If you want large quantities of steam quickly, a big firebox must be provided. The huge Beyer-Garratt engines seen on LMR tracks have been built with this in mind. British railways were laid out on rather skimpy lines in the beginning so no locomotive may be more than 13ft. 2in. high. To get an adequate size of boiler and deep firebox is difficult when it has to be built above driving wheel axles, so these locomotives have two bogie engines, carrying the boiler slung between them, the firebox almost reaching down to the rails. These are called "articulated" locomotives.

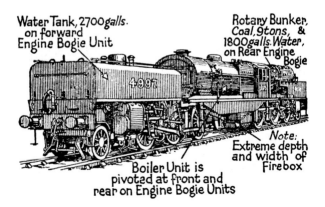

Water Tank, 2700 galls. on forward Engine Bogie Unit

Rotary Bunker, Coal, 9 tons, & 1800 galls. Water, on Rear Engine Bogie

4997

Note: Extreme depth and width of Firebox

Boiler Unit is pivoted at front and rear on Engine Bogie Units

Exhaust carried upwards by the deflected air currents due to Plates

How the deflected air currents carry away the exhaust.

SMOKE DEFLECTORS

Many locomotives have large sheet metal plates, variously described as " blinker plates," " smoke deflectors," and so on, set one on each side of their smokeboxes. The reason for these is easily explained. Economical working releases the exhaust steam at a comparatively low pressure so that it does not shoot up out of the chimney, but pours out softly. High-set boilers mean low chimneys. The result is that the steam and smoke blow down and obstruct the vision ahead of the engine crew. So deflectors are fitted to cause a strong stream of air to shoot upwards alongside the smokebox and carry the steam with it so that it trails away, clear of the boiler and cab, without being a nuisance.

THE TENDER AND
THE WATER PICK-UP

Now a few remarks upon the tender. When asked what the tender carries, most people answer " Coal." That is true but the first answer should really be " Water." An average tender carries about 5,000 gallons of it, weighing 22 tons. The coal may weigh anything between five and eight tons, according to the likely length of the daily run. The quantity of water may sound adequate but it disappears in about 150 miles, or even less. That distance governs the length of non-stop runs on the Southern Region on which there are no track water-troughs to enable the engines to replenish supplies on the run. This system dates back to 1859 when Mr. John Ramsbottom, locomotive superintendent of the L. & N.W.R. (now part of the LMR) laid down experimental troughs in North Wales to allow speeding up of the Irish mail trains. To-day, troughs are found at about 30-miles intervals almost

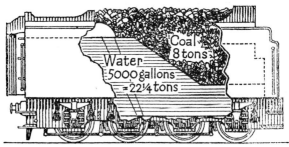

THE TENDER HOLDS WATER AND COAL

everywhere on the LMR main lines.   There is a set even in a tunnel in Yorkshire.

The pick-up gear in the tender consists of a scoop which can be lowered so that its open end just dips below the surface of the water in the trough.   A deflector, just in front of the scoop guides the water into it.   The water rushes up the pipe at the back of the scoop and is turned into the tender tank at the top by the deflecting dome.   Two thousand gallons can be gathered from a trough $\frac{1}{2}$-mile long in 40 seconds.

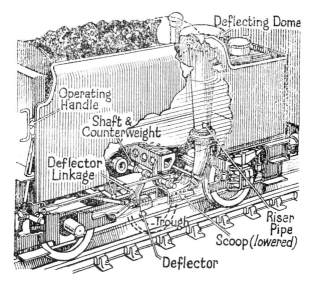

The water scoop is lowered when the locomotive is approaching the trough and raised again after the supply of water has been taken in.

LUBRICATION

Now a word on lubrication.   Gone are the days
when the fireman climbed around the locomotive with
an oilcan while the train was on the move.   Mechanical
lubricators supply all working parts with a constant
feed, particularly the axle bearings.   Cylinders are not
so easy to lubricate but by injecting oil into the steam
pipes, the steam carries it into the cylinders quite
satisfactorily.   Steam pressure is often employed to
force the oil wherever it is required, and the fireman
can see the oil flowing through little glass windows in
the lubricator in the cab.   Arrangements have to be
made to extract the oil from exhaust steam that passes
into the injector, as it would be dangerous to have it
going into the boiler and superheater.

Working parts that cannot be lubricated by way of
feed pipes get their oil from little boxes from which it
is fed by cotton wicks, or trimmings, the boxes being
filled at the beginning of each run.   Many working
parts on modern locomotives now have ball, or roller,
bearings (some of the links on valve gears for instance),
and often we find the axles of tenders have them.   So
far they have not been used much on driving axles
or connecting rods, although some American locomotives are running with roller bearings to the driving
wheels, as well as other working parts, and the LMR
are going to try them in the same way on some engines.

SPRINGING

We have not yet talked about springing the great weight of the engine—a very important matter. These springs have to be very massive. They are either of the laminated or flat leaf sort that can be seen on a smaller scale on freight wagons, or the coiled type. The laminated springs are sometimes coupled together at their ends by a pivoted bar. This "compensates" their action and evens out the load so that a heavy engine passing over gaps between rails at their joints or crossings does not bump as heavily as it might with individual springs. Driving wheel springs have to be especially massive to stand up to the additional load put on them by the driving effort and coupling rods.

THE BRAKES

Finally we come to the very important subject of brakes. It is easy to see how the brake blocks are pressed hard against the tyres of the wheels by levers, but what you cannot see is what moves the levers. When the engine is cold, and there is no steam to build up the necessary vacuum or pressure, or during an

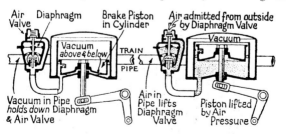

emergency, the levers can be pulled up to their work by a hand-operated screw on the tender.

Brakes are applied by the pressure of air and this is true whatever system is used, whether vacuum or compressed air (as in the Westinghouse system). The brake levers are worked by other levers operated by a piston in a cylinder.

With the vacuum brake this cylinder is a fairly big one and the piston is right at the bottom when the brake is off. The brake cylinders all along the train are connected by a single pipe tightly closed at the very end of the last coach. From this pipe and all the cylinders as much air as possible is drawn out by the ejector in the engine cab. This works somewhat like the injector: a jet of steam blowing into a pipe carries air along with it and all the air comes out of the brake cylinders. The steam passes along a fat pipe by the side of the boiler and into the smokebox, helping to draw up the fire as it escapes up the chimney.

We do not get a complete vacuum this way but the air pressure in the cylinders is reduced to a very small amount, not more than 5 lb. to the square inch, the pressure of the air outside being a little less than 15 lb. So, when the driver wants to put on the brakes he moves a lever that opens a valve admitting air from outside to a pipe connecting the undersides of all the cylinders. With a full admission this would give a pressure of $15 - 5 = 10$ lb. to the square inch over the whole piston area, amounting to a power of about $1\frac{1}{2}$ tons with a 21-inch cylinder as fitted to a locomotive. Multiply this by the power of the lever, equal to six or more, and you have some idea of the pressure against the wheel tyres when the brakes are fully applied.

With the Westinghouse type of brake no vacuum is employed. Instead, a steam-driven pump is at work keeping up a pressure of 50 lb. to the square inch in a reservoir connected to a pipe linking up all the brake cylinders in the train and on the engine. These brake cylinders are not so big as those for the vacuum type as the pressure is higher. Actually it is not as high as 50 lb. because the 15 lb. pressure of the atmosphere has to be subtracted from it. The brakes are released simply by opening a valve in the pressure pipe, allowing the high pressure air to escape.

Releasing the brakes of vacuum type is done by connecting the ejector to the undersides of the pistons and drawing out the air. The pistons fall by their own weight and that of the levers connected to them.

Some locomotives have a pump fitted to the crosshead of the piston rod (which, of course, goes on working all the time the engine is running). This is a vacuum pump and it takes some of the load off the ejector.

An important and necessary feature of the brake setup is that of automatic action in the event of breakage of the train pipe. This might be caused, for example, by the train breaking in two by failure of a coupling. A small leak can be a dreadful nuisance to the driver as it means the ejector has to be kept going fully all the time, but a broken or disconnected pipe would make it impossible for him to get the brakes off at all. His ejector would be drawing air through the system by way of the open end of the pipe.

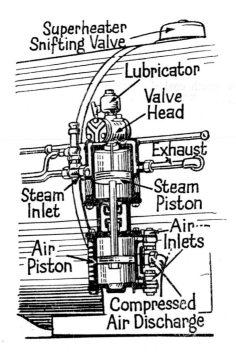

Superheater
Snifting Valve

Lubricator

Valve
Head

Exhaust

Steam
Inlet

Steam
Piston

Air
Inlets

Air
Piston

Compressed
Air Discharge

INSIDE THE WESTINGHOUSE AIR PUMP
ON THE SMOKE-BOX

THE LOCOMOTIVE'S APPETITE

How much coal does a big engine use when on a long run? Well, of course, that question has a lot of answers because so much depends upon the sort of coal, the weight of the train, the weather conditions and so on. But it might be a fair estimate to reckon that every mile calls for the burning of about 40 lb. of coal of good average quality and each pound boils away about 8 lb. of water in a big express locomotive of 4-6-0 or 4-6-2 type hauling a train of 500 tons—that is, about 14 or 15 coaches. The quantity will not be less than 35 lb. and may well be over 55 lb. which means some pretty hard work for the fireman on a long run. He will have to get a ton of coal through the small firing door practically every 50 miles. Not only has he to throw it straight and true through the door, but he has to spread it carefully over the fire to keep an even thickness of fuel everywhere. Just pitching it in would pile it up in the middle and would be absolutely useless. The far end of the firebox may well mean as much as a ten-foot throw.

Nor is this all that the fireman has to do. His is the responsibility for seeing that the water-level in the boiler is always well up. He looks after the lubricators and operates the water scoop. In addition to all this, he must be ready to check the signals with the driver.

ISBN 0-7110-2695-5

107
WHSmith

9 "780711"026957

Printed in England   £4.99

Ian Allan